MILLS & BOON®

The Art
of
Romance

Harlequin UK Ltd
An imprint of HarperCollinsPublishers
1 London Bridge Street
London
SE1 9GF

First published by Harlequin in 2016

Copyright © 2016 Harlequin UK Ltd
Patterns by Joe Bright and Shutterstock

ISBN 978-0-00-818183-3
Printed and bound in Spain

Introduction

Mills & Boon was founded in 1908, and our national love affair with romance has continued ever since.

For the bright young things of the 1920s, the sharp-suited and mini-skirted fashionistas of the 1960s, through to today's Tinder generation, love stories have always been the best kind of escapism.

As our lives get busier, it's never been more important to take time to sit down and appreciate the simple joy of romance. In this book, we've used our most iconic covers to chart the history of love in the last century.

Whether you use the beautiful original artwork as inspiration, or simply let your imagination lead the way, bringing these irresistible illustrations to life is the perfect way to celebrate the art of romance.

MERRY GOES THE TIME

ELEANOR FARNES

1920

Flappers – with their bobbed hair, short skirts, and love of partying – rule the jazz age.

BRODIE AND THE DEEP SEA

I·A·R·WYLIE

MILLS & BOON LONDON

AARRY RILEY

1923

F. Scott Fitzgerald writes some of the most enduring novels of the Jazz Age during the 1920s, including *This Side of Paradise, The Beautiful and Damned* and *The Great Gatsby.*

THE FORTUNE HUNTERS

Dennys

BY

C.N. & A.M. WILLIAMSON

1927

The first transatlantic telephone call is made from New York City to London, introducing a whole new way to say 'I love you'.

1935

After the 1930s, you no longer had to leave your holiday romance behind forever, as the newly introduced Air Mail service meant post could be sent across the Atlantic.

JENNIFER DISAPPEARS

SHEILDS.

JENNIFER CREELY

MAIRI O'NAIR

1937

Disney release *Snow White and the Seven Dwarfs*, their first feature-length animated film. The classic romance between Snow White and her Prince has gone on to entrance audiences for generations.

1938

Rebecca, Daphne Du Maurier's story of love, jealousy and obsession, is first published. Its unforgettable characters and famously anonymous narrator made it an instant classic, with an iconic Hitchcock adaptation to follow in 1940.

MAN–AND WAIF

Jan Tempest

1939

As the Second World War approaches, *We'll Meet Again* is released by Vera Lynn. It would go on to epitomise the tragedy of the war, resonating with soldiers separated from their families and sweethearts.

ONE OF THE FAMILY

MARY BURCHELL

1941

The invention of the microwave speeds up cooking and sparks
the beginning of convenience food. *Ping!*

1942

Casablanca, starring Humphrey Bogart and Ingrid Bergman, is released in cinemas. *Play it again, Sam!*

1944

Commercial television is developed in the 1940s – paving the way for public addresses, soap operas, chick flicks and box-set binges.

1944

After starring as Rhett Butler in 1939's *Gone With the Wind*,
Clark Gable – known as 'The King of Hollywood' rose to even
higher notoriety in the 1940s.

1945

As the war ends, *that* Times Square kiss is captured on camera, and V-J Day is celebrated across America.

1946

Frank Sinatra releases his first album. The star of swing and future Rat Pack member is considered timeless by many, with innumerable classic romantic hits to his name.

1946

Not even fashion could escape the war, with patriotic nautical themes, dark greens and khakis dominating the colour palettes, while trousers and wedges slowly replace dresses and more traditional heels.

THE

THORNY

ROSE

MARGARET MALCOLM

1947

Princess (later Queen) Elizabeth marries Philip Mountbatten at Westminster Abbey, in a ceremony broadcast to 200 million listeners around the world.

1947

The Diary of a Young Girl (or *The Diary of Anne Frank*) is published for the first time. A heart-breaking relic of the war, it has stood the test of time as an unforgettable account of courage and love in the face of adversity.

PRIDE
BEFORE
FALL

NAN SHARPE

1952

Following the death of George VI, his daughter is crowned Queen Elizabeth II. She would go on to become the longest-ruling monarch ever.

GRACE BEFORE MEAT

SARA SEALE

1952

Singin' in the Rain is released in cinemas. A light-hearted take on a 1920s production company's transition from silent film to 'talkies', it was an instant hit – thanks, in part, to its unforgettable eponymous song.

1953

A bored and sheltered princess finds love with a US Newsman in *A Roman Holiday,* starring Audrey Hepburn and Gregory Peck, which is released in cinemas this year.

1956

Heartbreak Hotel, Elvis Presley's first single to top the charts,
storms to number one.

BEGIN TO LIVE

ELEANOR BURFORD

1956

The 1950s was 'The Golden Age of Television', with more people than ever before owning a television. But that didn't stop Hollywood megastars, such as Marilyn Monroe and James Dean, finding fame in this decade.

ROMANCE GOES TENTING

PHYLLIS MATTHEWMAN

1958

After appearing in 1957's controversial film *And God Created Woman*, French actress Brigitte Bardot is firmly established as one of the most iconic sex symbols of the 1950s and 1960s.

1958

The 1950s saw commercial air travel and exotic locations become
a reality for the masses as the passenger jet enters service.

RED LOTUS

CATHERINE AIRLIE

1959

A plane transporting musicians Buddy Holly, Ritchie Valens, The Big Bopper and pilot Roger Peterson goes down in foggy conditions, killing all four on board. The tragedy is later termed *The Day the Music Died,* popularised in Don McLean's 1971 song 'American Pie'.

1962

Marilyn Monroe, perhaps the most iconic actress of all time, is found dead at home aged thirty-six. Despite being divorced at the time of her death, her ex-husband Joe DiMaggio, sent red roses to her grave in Los Angeles three times a week for the next twenty years.

Mills & Boon

THE HOUSE ON FLAMINGO CAY

Anne Weale

1964

After meeting on the set of *Cleopatra,* Elizabeth Taylor and
Richard Burton are married for the first time after a passionate
and very public affair.

1966

Mini-skirts and partying are the order of the day as young people celebrate a new kind of freedom. The infamous Summer of Love would follow in 1967.

BRITTLE BONDAGE

Rosalind Brett

1966

Lesley Lawson, widely known by the nickname Twiggy, becomes one of the most iconic models of the 'swinging sixties'.

THE STEPSISTERS
ELEANOR FARNES

1972

At the height of 1970s opulence, David Bowie launches Ziggy Stardust – a defining moment for pop and gender politics.

Mills & Boon

728

MAIDEN FLIGHT

Betty Beaty

1975

It was a good decade for facial-hair fans as, alongside flares and platform shoes, beards and sideburns came into fashion – for the first time since the 19th century!

Mills & Boon Classics

Betty Beaty

AMBER FIVE

1978

Grease, starring John Travolta and Olivia Newton-John, is released in cinemas. From the karaoke favourites to *that* pair of trousers, it's the ultimate make-over film and frequently voted the nation's favourite musical.

Mills & Boon

VALLEY OF THE MOON

Margaret Way

1980

With its boozy lunches and brick-size mobile phones, the 1980s were all about big business – and even bigger hair!

Mills & Boon Classics

Violet Winspear

LUCIFER'S ANGEL

1981

Prince Charles marries Lady Diana Spencer in what is still the most expensive wedding of all time. The ceremony had twenty-seven wedding cakes and was televised to 750 million people worldwide.

Mills & Boon

Best Seller Romance

BEWARE THE BEAST

Anne Mather

1985

In the 1980s, more is more! Bouffant perms and
ra-ra-skirts rule the catwalk, while power-dressing takes women
to the boardroom in style.

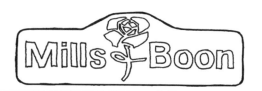

Mills & Boon

BEST SELLER ROMANCE

High Tide at Midnight

SARA CRAVEN

1988

Naomi Campbell is *the* model of the moment, and is named as
one of the six 'supermodels' of her generation.

Mills & Boon

ROMANCE

Dark Desiring

JACQUELINE BAIRD

1992

Cool Britannia rules the 1990s, with the sparring Gallagher brothers and their stadium-filling anthems set to keep all eyes on the Brit Pop music scene.

Mills & Boon

ROMANCE

A Family Affair

CHARLOTTE LAMB

1992

Kate Moss, with her waifish figure and rock-and-roll attitude, firmly establishes herself as one of the most famous faces of the decade.

Mills & Boon

ROMANCE

Secret Admirer

SUSAN NAPIER

1998

The BBC adaptation of *Pride and Prejudice,* starring Colin Firth as Fitzwilliam Darcy, is released. For many, Colin Firth's famous lake scene remains the most iconic on-screen Austen moment of all time.

MILLS & BOON®
Presents™

SHARON KENDRICK
One Bridegroom Required!

1999

As we count down to the millennium, the nation really can *party like it's 1999*. Who was your midnight kiss?

LYNNE GRAHAM

Contract Baby

2004

The Notebook is released in cinemas... and the world falls in love with Ryan Gosling.

2008

Mills & Boon celebrates its centenary – and a hundred years of breath-taking romance. And with 21,000 books sold a day (that's one every four seconds) it seems we're even bigger romance fans than ever!

Anne
Stuart

RUTHLESS

HISTORICAL

2010

After their success on TV talent show *The X Factor,* boy band One Direction are formed and millions of teenagers lose their hearts!

2012

One year after her marriage to Prince William, Kate Middleton falls pregnant with Prince George.

2014

A-listers flock to the nuptials of selfie-queen Kim Kardashian and mega-famous pop star Kanye West at the Forte di Belvedere in Florence, Italy, with Instagram updates keeping the stars' fans in the loop throughout the day.

2015

Princess Charlotte, a little sister for Prince George, is born to Prince William and Kate Middleton.

BOUND BY THE

Billionaire's

BABY

CATHY WILLIAMS